STICKER DRESS

EXPLORERS

Illustrated by Diego Diaz

Written by Struan Reid
Designed by Lucy Wain
Historical consultant: Dr. Anne Millard

CONTENTS

You'll find all the sticker pages in the middle of the book. When you see this sign ✳ it means the person it's next to is a real explorer or another real character from history.

Usborne Quicklinks
For links to websites to find out more about explorers go to the Usborne Quicklinks Website at www.usborne-quicklinks.com and type in the keywords 'sticker dressing explorers'. Please read our internet safety guidelines on the Usborne Quicklinks Website.

Around Africa

Pharaoh Necho of Egypt has hired sailors from Phoenicia, in the eastern Mediterranean, to explore the African coast. He has sent one of his officials to talk to the sailors before they set out. The official wears a tunic of fine linen and a striped headdress, while the sailors wear linen tunics and wool cloaks.

Phoenician captain

Egyptian official

Phoenician sailor

3

Reaching America

It is the year 1000, and a Viking leader named Leif Ericsson and his men have left their base in Greenland to sail westward and explore new lands to settle. They have reached the eastern coast of North America. They're wearing thick wool shirts and breeches to keep them warm, and cloaks with big brooches.

Ship's pilot

Viking sailor

Leif Ericsson ✳

Overland to China

An Italian merchant named Marco Polo has spent many months on a journey from Venice overland to China. He has finally arrived at the Chinese border where he is met by a guard and an official sent by the emperor. Marco wears clothes of thick leather and wool. The guard wears protective metal and leather clothing, and the official is dressed in a silk coat and felt hat and boots.

Border guard

Marco Polo ✳   Chinese official

It is 1325, and a rich Moroccan called Ibn Battuta has made a pilgrimage to Mecca in Arabia. Now he is exploring parts of the Middle East, and will travel to Africa and on to the Far East. Here he's at a desert oasis where he has stopped for the night. His cotton headdress and fine wool cloak keep him cool in the day, and warm at night. The guard wears thick leather clothes and a helmet.

Guard

Ibn Battuta ✷   Merchant

Across the Indian Ocean

It's the 1400s, and Admiral Cheng Ho is on an expedition for the Chinese emperor. For the next 30 years he will make seven sea journeys that take him as far as the Persian Gulf and the east coast of Africa. He has just been presented with a present of a giraffe for the emperor. He wears a silk hat and silk robes embroidered with the emperor's dragon symbol. The African chieftain wears patterned robes and a heavy gold necklace.

African chieftain

Cheng Ho ☀   Giraffe keeper   II

Westward to China

Christopher Columbus and his men left Spain on August 3 1492, in search of a westward sea route to China. They have been sailing for more than two months and at last they have reached land. They think they have finally arrived in China, but in fact they have discovered the Bahama Islands in the West Indies. Columbus is wearing thick wool breeches, leather boots and a short wool cloak.

Christopher Columbus ✳

AROUND AFRICA

Follow the numbers and arrows to add the stickers in the right order.

① Egyptian official's sandals

② Robe

① Phoenician sailor's sandals

① Phoenician captain's sandals

② Robe

② Skirt

③ Cloak

③ Collar

④ Headdress

Scales

③ Headband

⑤ Bracelets

Pages 2-3

REACHING AMERICA

Follow the numbers and arrows to add the stickers in the right order.

① Viking sailor's boots

② Cloak

③ Sword

① Ship's pilot's tunic and cloak

② Axe

③ Helmet

④ Shield

① Leif Ericsson's boots

② Shirt and cloak

③ Helmet

④ Bracelet

⑤ Spear

OVERLAND TO CHINA

Follow the numbers and arrows to add the stickers in the right order.

① Chinese border guard's boots

② Helmet

② Breeches

③ Protective tunic

① Marco Polo's shoes

③ Coat

④ Hat

Spear

④ Wrist guards

② Tunic

① Chinese official's boots

③ Hat

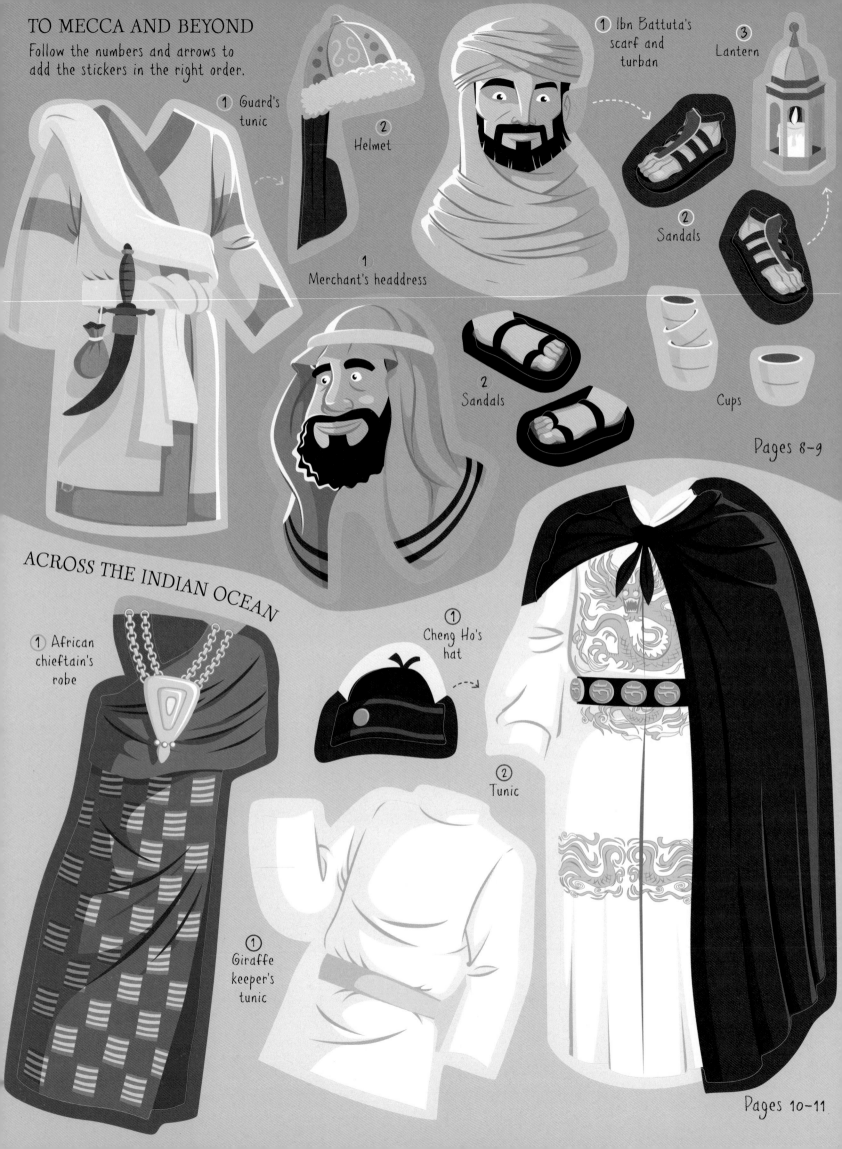

TO MECCA AND BEYOND

Follow the numbers and arrows to add the stickers in the right order.

1 Guard's tunic

2 Helmet

1 Merchant's headdress

1 Ibn Battuta's scarf and turban

2 Sandals

3 Lantern

2 Sandals

Cups

Pages 8-9

ACROSS THE INDIAN OCEAN

1 African chieftain's robe

1 Cheng Ho's hat

2 Tunic

1 Giraffe keeper's tunic

Pages 10-11

WESTWARD TO CHINA

Follow the numbers and arrows to add the stickers in the right order.

Rope

① Christopher Columbus's breeches

Flag

② Boots

③ Jacket and cloak

④ Hat

Page 12

THE ROUTE TO INDIA

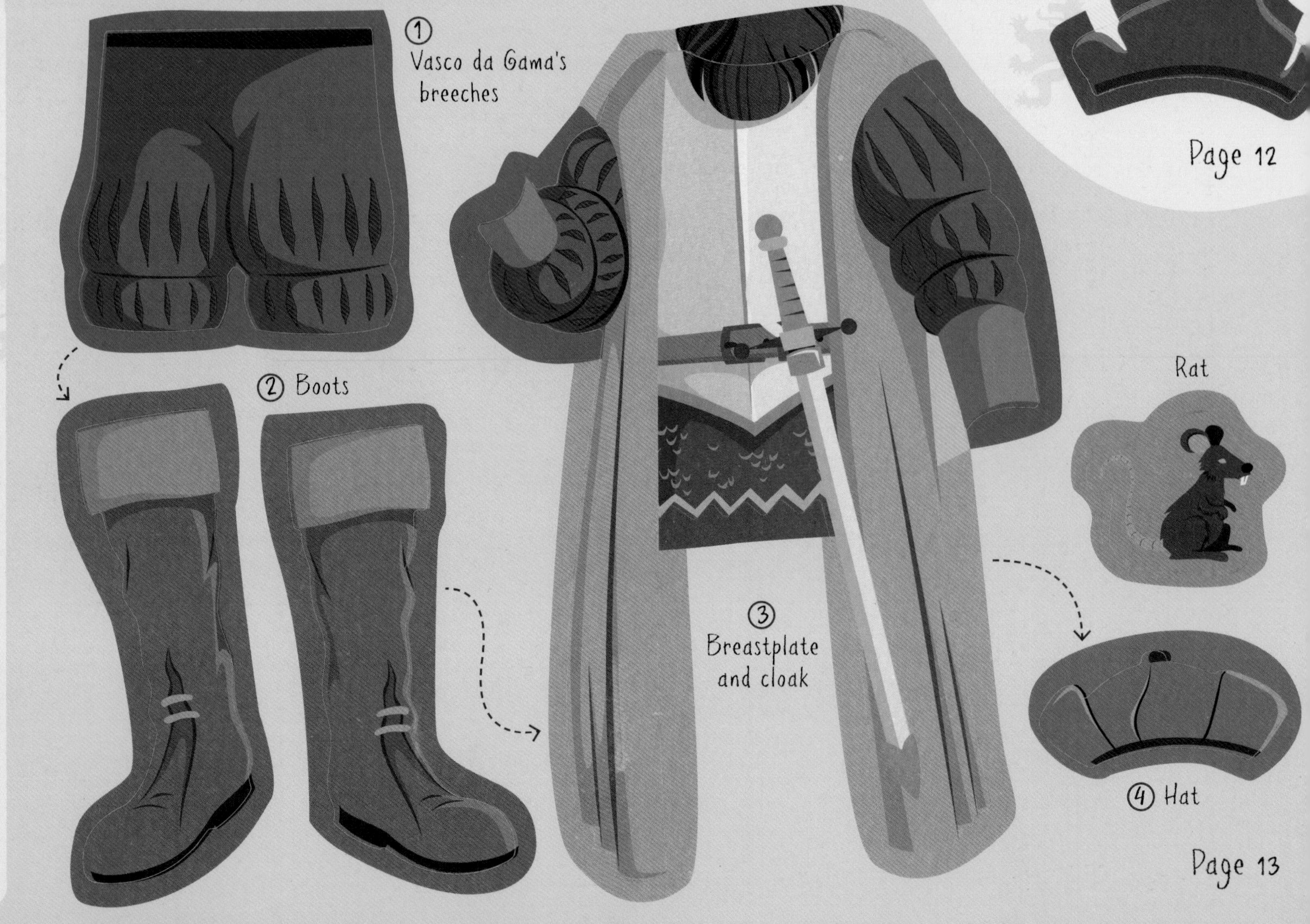

① Vasco da Gama's breeches

② Boots

③ Breastplate and cloak

④ Hat

Rat

Page 13

AROUND THE WORLD
Follow the numbers and arrows to add the stickers in the right order.

① Ferdinand Magellan's breeches

② Boots

① Ship's captain's breeches

Ferdinand Magellan's sword

② Boots

③ Jacket

③ Jacket

④ Cloak

⑤ Hat

Ferdinand Magellan's cross-staff, used to calculate distances

① Sailor's shirt

② Sailor's leggings

③ Shoes

④ Hat

④ Headband

Pages 14-15

AUSTRALIA AND THE PACIFIC

Follow the numbers and arrows to
add the stickers in the right order.

① Maori chief's feather headdress

① James Cook's shoes

① Sailor's shirt

② Breeches

② Cloak

② Leggings

③ Rifle

③ Waistcoat and coat

④ Headband

③ Necklace

⑤ Telescope

④ Paddle

Kiwi

⑥ Map

⑤ Tricorn hat

④ Sextant used to calculate distances

DEEP INTO AFRICA

Follow the numbers and arrows to add the stickers in the right order.

① David Livingstone's shoes

① African guard's robe

① Tribal chief's headdress

② Robe

② Shirt

③ Cloak

③ Trousers

③ Gun

② Headdress

④ Bracelets

④ Shirt and jacket

⑤ Stick

⑤ Ankle bands

⑥ Sun hat

Pages 18-19

TO THE SOUTH POLE

Follow the numbers and arrows to add the stickers in the right order.

① Roald Amundsen's hat

② Coat

③ Gloves

④ Boots

① Olav Bjaaland's coat

① Oscar Wisting's gloves

③ Skis and ski boots

② Gloves

② Coat

③

③ Skis and ski boots

UNDER THE SEA

Follow the numbers and arrows to add the stickers in the right order.

① Jacques Cousteau's wetsuit

⑤ Underwater camera

④ Fins

③ Mask

② Harness carries oxygen tanks

① Scientist's shorts

② Sandals

③ Wind gauge

① Ship's captain's shorts

② Socks and sandals

③ Hat

Page 22-23

UP TO THE MOON

① Neil Armstrong's space helmet

② Boots

③ Gloves

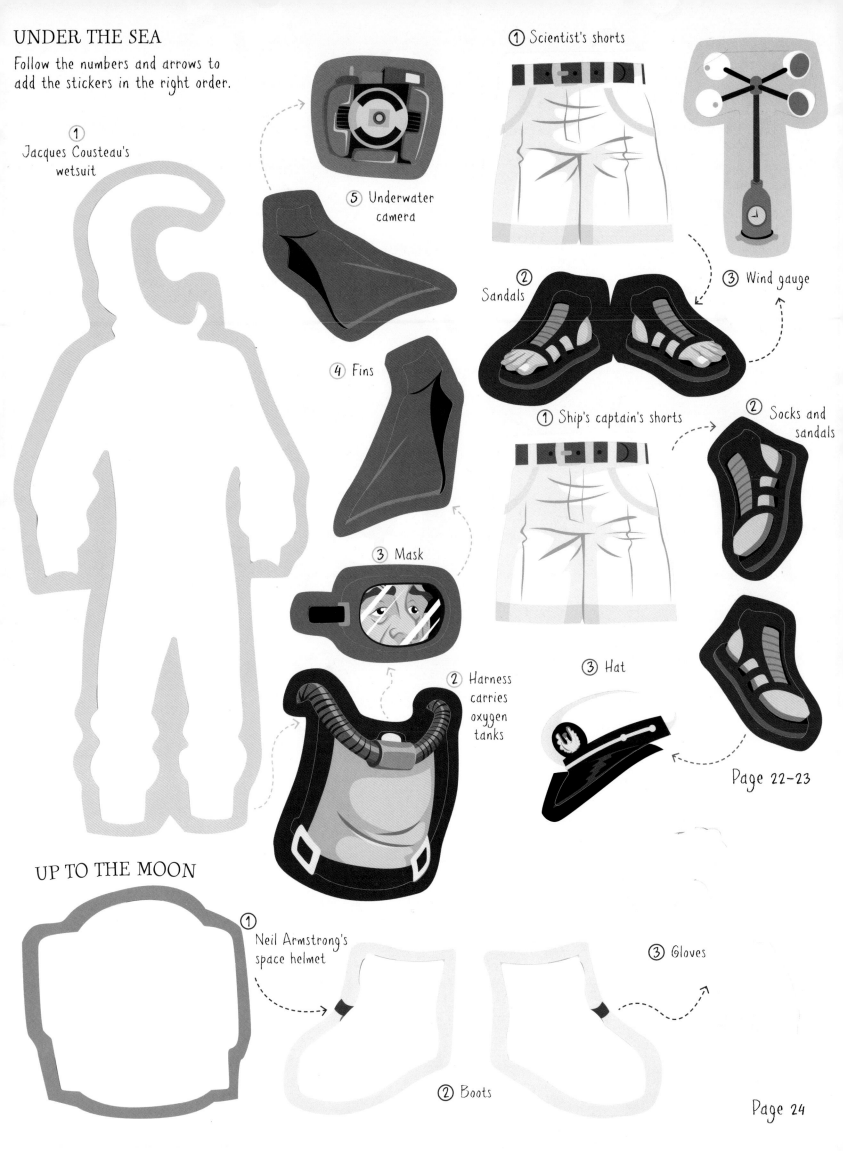

The route to India

It is July 1497, and a Portuguese explorer called Vasco da Gama is about to set sail from the port of Lisbon. He hopes to establish trade contacts with India. Over the next two years he and his crew will sail around Africa and on to southwest India. Da Gama is wearing the clothes of a royal courtier, with a fur-trimmed velvet cloak and velvet hat, and tall leather boots.

Vasco da Gama ✳

Around the world

It's September 1519, and the first expedition to sail all the way around the world has just left Spain. It is led by a Portuguese nobleman named Ferdinand Magellan, with five ships and 260 men. But when the expedition returns to Spain three years later, in 1522, only one ship will have survived the journey, and Magellan himself will be dead.

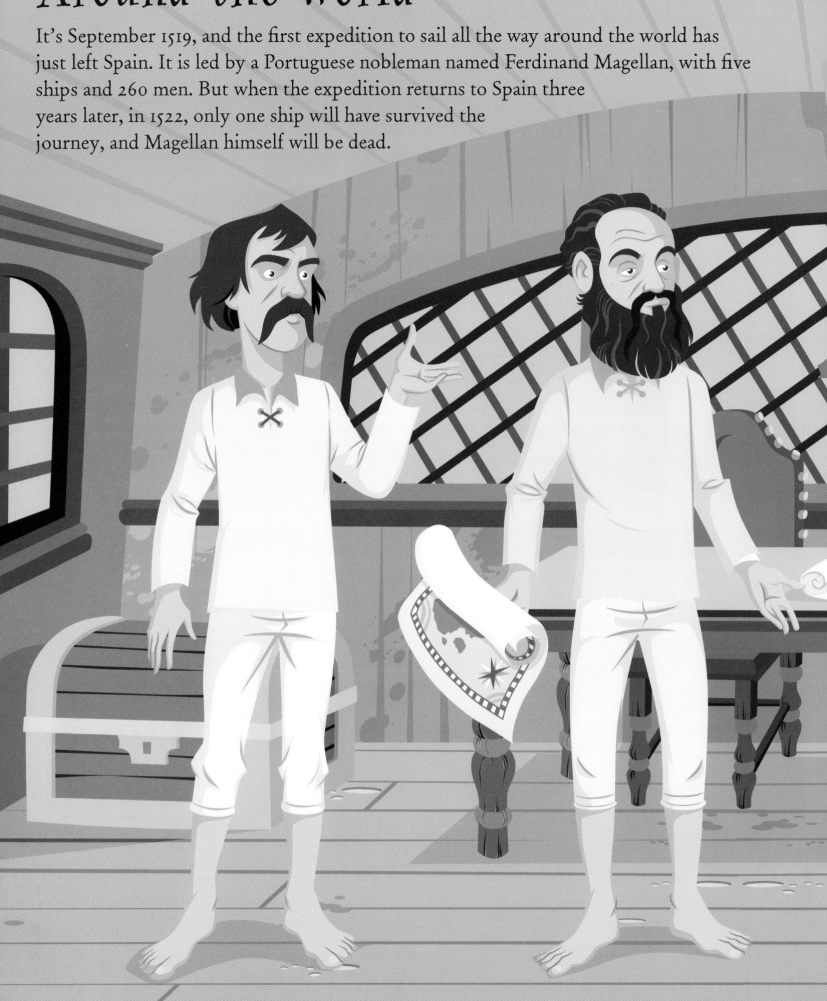

Ship's captain

Ferdinand Magellan ✳

Sailor

Australia and the Pacific

In 1769, James Cook set sail from England in his ship the *Endeavour* to explore the islands in the Pacific Ocean, New Zealand and Australia. He and his men have arrived on the New Zealand coast where they are met by local Maori warriors. The Maori chief is wearing a long cloak made of feathers. Cook wears a long wool frock coat, wool breeches and leather shoes, while his sailors are wearing baggy linen shirts and leggings.

Maori chief

James Cook ✴   Sailor

17

Deep into Africa

From the 1850s, a Scottish missionary named David Livingstone spent many years exploring Africa and trying to stamp out the slave trade. He also became the first European to see the vast waterfalls known locally as 'the smoke that thunders', which he renamed the Victoria Falls. Here he is wearing thick cotton and linen clothes that help protect him against the fierce sun and insect bites.

Tribal chief

David Livingstone ✳   African guard

19

To the South Pole

In October 1911, five Norwegian explorers led by Roald Amundsen set out across Antarctica for the South Pole. After two months of battling across a bitterly cold landscape, they've finally arrived and they're planting the flag of Norway at the South Pole. They're wearing light but very warm fur clothes and they travel on skis while their supplies are pulled by husky dogs.

Olav Bjaaland ✳   Roald Amundsen ✳

Oscar Wisting ✳

Under the sea

In 1943, French explorer Jacques Cousteau designed the first aqualung, making possible a new era of underwater exploration. He has just returned from one of his dives. He is wearing a rubber diving suit and goggles, and holding an underwater camera.

Jacques Cousteau ✳

Scientist

Ship's captain

Up to the moon

On July 21, 1969 astronauts Neil Armstrong and 'Buzz' Aldrin become the first people ever to step onto the moon. Since there is no oxygen on the moon, they wear special clothes and helmets so they can breathe while they walk around.

Neil Armstrong ✳